PRICE
8 00
IN CANADA

# BELA BARTOK
## CONCERTO
### . FOR ORCHESTRA

# BOOSEY & HAWKES
## MUSIC PUBLISHERS LIMITED

LONDON · PARIS · BONN · JOHANNESBURG · SYDNEY · TORONTO · NEW YORK

MADE IN ENGLAND                    NET PRICE

*First performance on December 1st, 1944, by the Boston Symphony Orchestra under the direction of Dr. Serge Koussevitzky, at Carnegie Hall, New York.*

## INSTRUMENTATION

3 Flutes (3rd doubling Piccolo)

3 Oboes (3rd doubling Cor Anglais)

3 Clarinets in B♭ and A (3rd doubling Bass Clarinet)

3 Bassoons (3rd doubling Double Bassoon)

4 Horns in F

3 Trumpets in C (4th Trumpet ad lib.)

2 Tenor Trombones

Bass Trombone

Tuba

Timpani

Side Drum

Bass Drum

Tam-Tam

Cymbals

Triangle

2 Harps

Strings

*Duration:* approximately 37 minutes

# CONCERTO FOR ORCHESTRA

BÉLA BARTÓK

# I

## (INTRODUZIONE)

B. & H. 9009

5

B.&H. 9009

\*) always use a soft (cardboard) mute.

13

B. & H. 9009

16

413

424

424

near the sound-board with an appropriately
shaped wooden (if possible metal) stick

27

B.& H. 9009

28

B. & H. 9009

Duration of 1st movement approx. 9'48"

# II
## (GIUOCO DELLE COPPIE)

34

B. & H. 9009

38

44

46

Duration of 2nd movement approx. 6'17"

# III
## (ELEGIA)

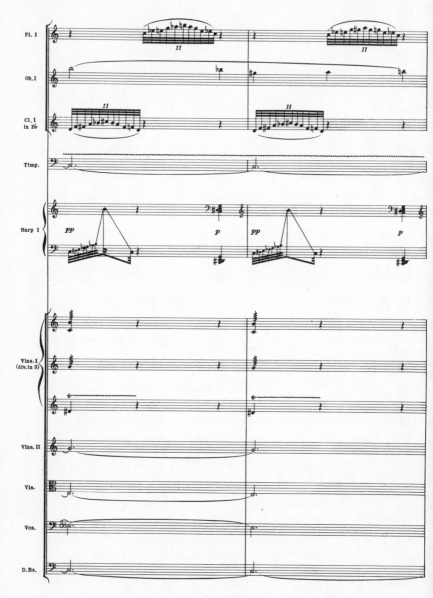

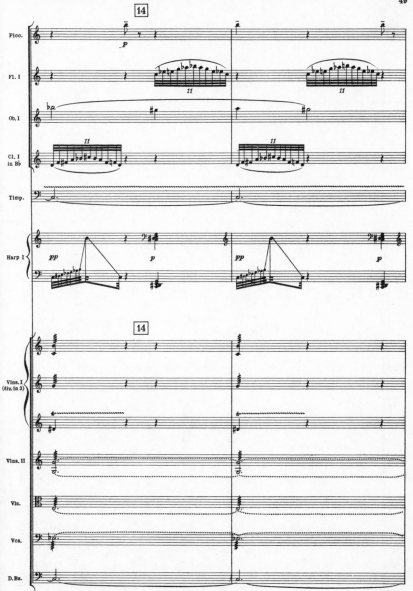

50

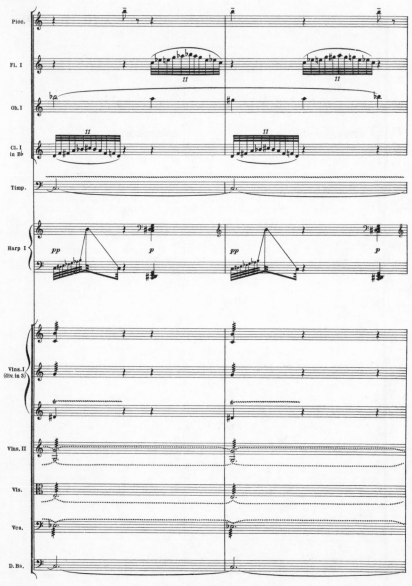

62

63

B.& H. 9009

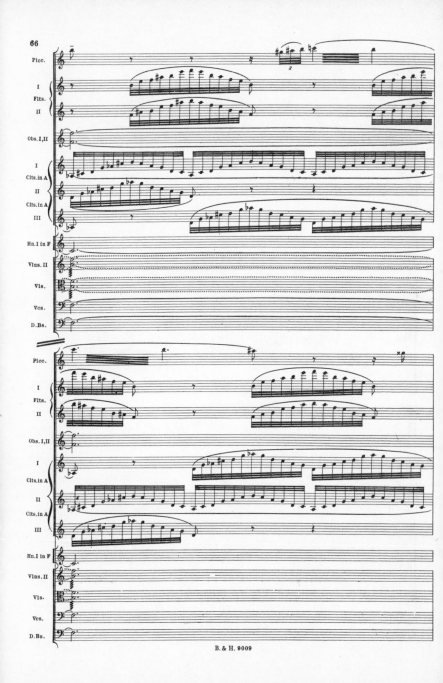

Duration of 3rd movement approx. 7′11″

# IV
## (INTERMEZZO INTERROTTO)

* If the Flute has no low *b*, 1st Bassoon will play: and Flute tacet.

*real sound:

70

73

B.& H. 9009

74

B.& H. 9009

76

Duration of 4th movement approx. 4' 8"

# V
## (FINALE)

*always non spiccato (i.e. legato)

B. & H. 9009

88

110

B. & H. 9009

114

119

126

B.& H. 9009

129

\* as near the bridge as possible.

132

B.& H.9009

138

142

144

Duration of 5th movement approx. 8'52"
Duration of the whole work ca.37'

*Alternative ending*